How to Be More
PADDINGTON

Collection first published in hardback in Great Britain by HarperCollins *Children's Books* in 2020

1 3 5 7 9 10 8 6 4 2

ISBN: 978-0-00-843871-5

HarperCollins *Children's Books* is a division of HarperCollins*Publishers* Ltd.

Text copyright © The Estate of Michael Bond 1958–2020
Illustrations copyright © Peggy Fortnum and HarperCollins*Publishers* Ltd 1958–2020

Colour illustrations adapted by Mark Burgess from the originals by Peggy Fortnum

Printed in Europe

MIX
Paper from
responsible sources
FSC™ C007454

This book is produced from independently certified FSC™ paper to ensure responsible forest management.
Find out more about HarperCollins and the environment at www.harpercollins.co.uk/green

How to Be More
PADDINGTON

MICHAEL BOND

A BOOK OF KINDNESS

ILLUSTRATED BY **PEGGY FORTNUM**

HarperCollins *Children's Books*

"I wish there were more
bears about like you."

One of the very nice things about being an author is that you are never alone. The characters you have invented travel around with you and are always to hand when you need them, which can be a great comfort as you go through life.

I count myself fortunate in having Paddington as a friend. It's rather like having a built-in resident guru. Although his head is often in the clouds, he has his feet firmly on the ground and he has a strong sense of right and wrong. Confronted by a problem, I often find myself wondering how he would deal with it, and mentally take note of his advice.

MICHAEL BOND, 2008

BEING *friendly*

"When Mrs Brown saw my
label and read the words,
'Please look after
this bear. Thank you!'
she said at once I must
come home with them."

"Young Mr Brown has a habit of

*bringing people
closer together.*"

BEING *well meaning*

"Different people
have different ideas
about *being good*.
All the same, he looks
the sort of bear that
means well."

"Things are always
happening to me.
I'm that sort
of bear."

BEING *well meaning*

Paddington was usually

the first to offer

his services, almost always

with disastrous results.

"Bears are good
at mending things."

"I'm sure you
did your best
and you *meant well.*
Those are two of the
most important
things in life."

BEING *helpful*

"Willing paws
make light work."

BEING *grateful*

Paddington began making a list of

all the nice things

about being a bear and living with

the Browns. The list was so long

he nearly ran out of paper.

To show how *grateful* he was,

he disposed of the entire contents

and then washed the jar

spotlessly clean afterwards.

With his sparkler, he waved

Thank you, Mr Gruber,

for a lovely day out.

The only person who noticed was

Mr Gruber himself, but that

was really all that mattered.

"Aunt Lucy taught me to

count my blessings.

It's the first thing she does

when she wakes in the morning.

She says nine times out of ten

you have more than

you think you have.

"I've been counting my blessings.

Except, I do mine *before* I go to sleep.

I have so many I may not

have time tomorrow."

"We often take for granted the things that *mean the most* to us. Something we should never, *ever* do, especially when it comes to bears."

BEING *thoughtful*

"It's my Aunt Lucy's birthday
in August and she says
flowers always
brighten things up.
I thought I could send her a picture
she can keep by her bed."

He held the plate up
for the others to see.
"I've licked it
clean so you
can use it again
if you want to."

"I think I may pick some flowers for the Queen."

He enjoyed giving
his own presents
best of all.

Feeling under his hat,

he produced a sandwich.

"You can try this one

if you like. I made it myself

the week before last."

"I always share my buns
with Mr Gruber when we
have our elevenses and
I break them in half."

BEING *positive*

He wasn't the sort of bear
who believed in doing
things by halves.

Paddington believed in

looking on the bright side.

If he did the wallpapering really well,

the others might not even notice

the mess he'd made.

"This is the sort of day out
I like, Mr Gruber!"

Paddington announced, as he took

a jar of marmalade from his suitcase

and began making a sandwich.

BEING *wise*

Paddington was a surprising bear

in many ways and he had

a strong sense of

right and wrong.

"Aunt Lucy is very wise.
If it wasn't for her
I wouldn't be here at all.
Besides, she taught me
all I know."

"Look before you leap –
especially on a wet day."

"It's a *wise* **bear** who
knows which side of his
bread is buttered
before it falls to the ground."

"More haste, less speed.
Especially with paws."

BEING *Paddington*

Paddington had become *so much a part of things* it was almost impossible to picture life without him.

"Aunt Lucy gave me
a picture of herself so that
I wouldn't forget her.
But, of course, I never would.
I take it with me
wherever I go."

"*You're a very privileged person* to have breakfast in bed on a *weekday*!"

"He can't help
being sticky."

"Mrs Bird says
*I am worth my
weight in gold,*
which is very nice to know.
I tested myself on the bathroom
scales the other day."

"I wonder whether it's
just Paddington,
or whether all bears are
born under a
lucky star!"

"Let's have a chorus of
*'For he's a jolly good
bear cub'."*

"It's nice having a bear
about the house."

In my next life – if there is such a thing – I wouldn't mind being a bear. Provided, of course, I could be a bear like Paddington!

MICHAEL BOND, 2008